GOD'S PRESCRIPTION FOR
ENHANCING YOUR LOVE LIFE

LOVE, SEX & LASTING RELATIONSHIPS

CHIPINGRAM

Love, Sex & Lasting Relationships

CONTENTS

Love, Sex & Lasting Relationships

by Chip Ingram

It seems everybody these days wants love, sex, and a relationship that lasts. It's talked about on TV, portrayed in the movies, and is the most common theme of popular music.

But here's the question: if all our resources are focused on the pursuit of true love, great sex, and meaningful relationships, why are we drifting further and further from all three? Research clearly shows that love, family, and yes, even sex, are more elusive than ever. In the wake of the free-love generation, divorce has become an epidemic. As a result, generations of children are struggling to define the missing pieces of the relationships they've been denied and are now unable to cultivate in their own families. Meanwhile, sexual dissatisfaction has become the centerpiece of books, talk shows, and the booming pharmaceutical business. With all that turmoil, fewer and fewer relationships stand a chance of lasting.

At the root of it all is a belief system poisoned by hidden distortions. Without realizing it, we've bought into an approach to love that simply doesn't work.

But it doesn't have to be this way! In *Love, Sex & Lasting Relationships*, we'll uncover God's prescription for experiencing true love, maximum sexual satisfaction, and relationships that last a lifetime. It's an ancient approach that still bears a revolutionary spirit. Let's dig in together!

Keep Pressin' Ahead,

Hollywood's Formula for Lasting, Loving Relationships

INTRODUCTION

Everybody wants love. In fact, our search for love is the number one theme of today's popular movies, music, and literature. It preoccupies our hearts and shapes our life's pursuits. At the deepest level, we were created to connect with another person spiritually, emotionally, and even physically.

So here's the question. If we've been at this so long, how come we're so bad at it? Why are most of those love songs about break-ups, pain, dysfunctional relationships, and unfulfilled dreams? If God created us for love, why is it so difficult to find it?

Hollywood's Formula for Lasting, Loving Relationships

Video Notes

I. HOLLYWOOD'S PRESCRIPTION FOR LASTING RELATIONSHIPS

1. _____ the right person.

2. _____ in love.

3. _____ your hopes and dreams of future fulfillment on that person.

4. If _____ occurs, repeat steps 1, 2, and 3.

II. THE RESULTS

III. GOD'S PRESCRIPTION
FOR LASTING RELATIONSHIPS

¹Therefore be imitators of God, as beloved children; ²and walk in love, just as Christ also loved you, and gave Himself up for us, an offering and a sacrifice to God as a fragrant aroma. ~ **Ephesians** 5:1-2 **(NASB)**

1. _____ the right person.

2. _____ in love.

3. _____ your hope on God and seek to please Him through your relationship.

4. When failure occurs, repeat steps 1, 2, and 3.

IV. THE RESULTS

*"Marriage is not so much about **finding** someone as it is **being** someone."*

~ *Charles Shedd, from* Letters to Karen

Discussion Questions

1. What are some examples of popular movies, music, television, magazines, etc. that sell Hollywood's prescription for lasting relationships?

2. How have the things you watch, read, and listen to shaped what you believe about love and sex? In what ways have you bought into Hollywood's prescription for lasting relationships?

3. In your pursuit of a lasting relationship, have you been more focused on finding someone or on becoming someone? What has been your result?

4. Which is easier: To become an imitator of God or an imitator of a Hollywood role model? Explain.

5. Of all the qualities you look for in a mate, which ones do you think will be the most important to you long term? Do you possess these qualities? If not, what will you do this week in your pursuit to "become the right person"?

Hollywood's Formula for Lasting, Loving Relationships

SESSION 1 KEYS

- Popular culture tells us: "Find the right person and fall in love."

- God tells us: "Become the right person and walk in love."

ACTION STEPS

It's important to look back over your life and consider the different influences that have shaped the way you approach love. Was your idea of "love" impacted by a favorite TV show, a favorite movie, or a group of friends?

In the chart below, list the most influential factors in forming your understanding of love. Then give a brief "statement of belief" to describe what you were taught to believe as a result of your exposure to each influence.

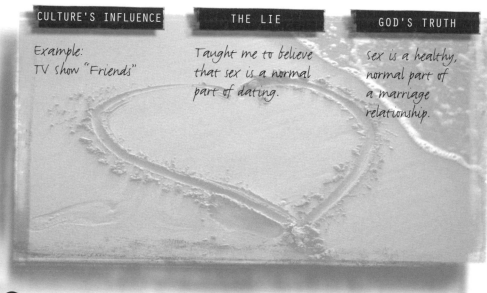

CULTURE'S INFLUENCE	THE LIE	GOD'S TRUTH
Example: TV show "Friends"	Taught me to believe that sex is a normal part of dating.	Sex is a healthy, normal part of a marriage relationship.

AT HOME

God created love and sex. That makes Him the best source for advice on cultivating a lasting relationship. As we learned in this session, the first step to adopting His approach to love is to become an imitator of God. In the spaces below, list two or three steps you could take this week to become an imitator of God so you are prepared when He brings a mate into your life.

MEMORY VERSE

Therefore be imitators of God, as beloved children; and walk in love, just as Christ also loved you, and gave Himself up for us, an offering and a sacrifice to God as a fragrant aroma.
~ *Ephesians 5:1-2 (NASB)*

Two Models for Lasting Relationships

INTRODUCTION

Our distorted understanding of love is one of the greatest plagues in our culture today. We don't know how to *be* in love because, in part, we don't understand how to *fall* in love. What should it look like to start down the path to a lasting relationship? On one hand, Hollywood tells us how to do it. But God's method is entirely different. As a result we drift along, following our feelings and hoping for the best.

Just as He created love, sex, and lasting relationships, God also created a set of principles that can guide us with confidence as we cultivate these important areas of our lives.

Two Models for Lasting Relationships

Video Notes

HOLLYWOOD'S FORMULA

spiritual
social
psychological
emotional
physical

GOD'S PRESCRIPTION

physical
emotional
psychological
social
spiritual

1. Ask: Is this person a committed _____?

2. Observe the person _____.

3. Get to _____ each other.

4. Keep your emotions behind _____ lead.

5. Come together _____.

Two Models for Lasting Relationships

PERSONAL EVALUATION & ANALYSIS

Which triangle most represents your approach to building lasting relationships?

Which model would you like your present and/or future relationships to look like?

What specific steps do you need to take to begin implementing God's secret to a lasting relationship?

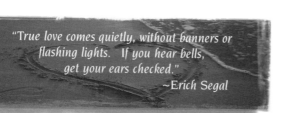

"True love comes quietly, without banners or flashing lights. If you hear bells, get your ears checked."
~Erich Segal

Two Models for Lasting Relationships

Discussion Questions

1. How successful has your current approach been in developing and sustaining long-term, healthy relationships that include all areas of intimacy — the spiritual, emotional, and physical?

2. What is the difference between "falling in love" and "walking in love"?

3. When it comes to a relationship with another person, what does it mean to "fix your hope on God" rather than on the other person?

4. What are some of the natural consequences of getting the pyramids Chip explained out of order? Give examples.

5. What is the hardest part about making corrections once the process has started incorrectly? What steps would you have to take to make corrections in your life?

Two Models for Lasting Relationships

- The message of society emphasizes the physical and emotional connection first, then the spiritual last.

- God emphasizes the spiritual component first and the physical component as the crowning celebration of intimacy.

ACTION STEPS

Spend some time alone with God in prayer and answer honestly the three questions in the personal evaluation and analysis.

Then,
If you're single, schedule some time with your accountability partner and outline for them the steps you wish to take in "becoming the right person."

If you're dating, set aside some time together to discuss honestly which model you have been following and set goals for how you would like to change.

If you're married, schedule some time with your spouse and outline some ways that you can begin to model God's prescription for your relationship.

Two Models for Lasting Relationships

AT HOME

It can be difficult to face up to the reality that our relationships aren't in perfect alignment with God's plan. But God is a God of mercy and love, not hardship and denial. As overwhelming as it may seem to consider revamping your relationship with a significant other, use the space below to describe one step that you need to take this week to begin aligning your love life with God's plan. If you are single, describe one commitment you need to make to yourself to ensure you follow God's approach to falling in love.

MEMORY VERSE

*Above all else, guard your heart,
for it is the wellspring of life.*
~ Proverbs 4:23 (NIV)

Before You "Fall in Love"

INTRODUCTION

You exchange a quick glance, followed by a warm, inviting smile. The attraction is suddenly intoxicating. Your heart races just a bit. A wonderful, euphoric feeling begins to flood your body.

Is it love? Maybe. But most likely it's another phenomenon described in the Bible. And while it shares a close relationship with love, it should never be mistaken for it. In fact, in our culture today, most of our "love baggage" - the heartaches and pains - could be avoided if we simply understood the difference between love and this other phenomenon from Scripture.

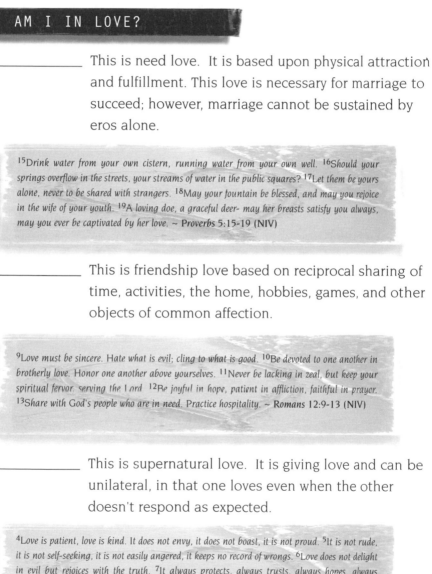

Before You "Fall in Love"

Video Notes

I. AM I IN LOVE?

_____ This is need love. It is based upon physical attraction and fulfillment. This love is necessary for marriage to succeed; however, marriage cannot be sustained by eros alone.

> ¹⁵Drink water from your own cistern, running water from your own well. ¹⁶Should your springs overflow in the streets, your streams of water in the public squares? ¹⁷Let them be yours alone, never to be shared with strangers. ¹⁸May your fountain be blessed, and may you rejoice in the wife of your youth. ¹⁹A loving doe, a graceful deer- may her breasts satisfy you always, may you ever be captivated by her love. ~ Proverbs 5:15-19 (NIV)

_____ This is friendship love based on reciprocal sharing of time, activities, the home, hobbies, games, and other objects of common affection.

> ⁹Love must be sincere. Hate what is evil; cling to what is good. ¹⁰Be devoted to one another in brotherly love. Honor one another above yourselves. ¹¹Never be lacking in zeal, but keep your spiritual fervor, serving the Lord. ¹²Be joyful in hope, patient in affliction, faithful in prayer. ¹³Share with God's people who are in need. Practice hospitality. ~ Romans 12:9-13 (NIV)

_____ This is supernatural love. It is giving love and can be unilateral, in that one loves even when the other doesn't respond as expected.

> ⁴Love is patient, love is kind. It does not envy, it does not boast, it is not proud. ⁵It is not rude, it is not self-seeking, it is not easily angered, it keeps no record of wrongs. ⁶Love does not delight in evil but rejoices with the truth. ⁷It always protects, always trusts, always hopes, always perseveres. ⁸Love never fails. But where there are prophecies, they will cease; where there are tongues, they will be stilled; where there is knowledge, it will pass away.
> ~ 1 Corinthians 13:4-8 (NIV)

Before You "Fall in Love"

II. IS IT LOVE OR INFATUATION?

THE TEST:

Test # 1- ___Time___

Love grows, and all growth requires time.
Infatuation may come on suddenly.

Test # 2- ___Knowledge___

Love grows out of an appraisal of all the known
characteristics of the other person. Infatuation
may arise from an acquaintance with only one or a
few of these characteristics.

Test # 3- _____

Love is other-person-centered. It is outgoing.
It results in sharing. Infatuation is self-centered.

Test # 4- ___Singularity___

Genuine love is centered on one person only.
An infatuated person may be "in love" with two
or more persons simultaneously.

Adapted from *Marriage for Moderns* by Dr. Henry Bowman

Before You "Fall in Love"

Discussion Questions

1. Have you ever been infatuated? Describe.

2. How would you describe the difference between the biblical concept of infatuation and the biblical concept of love?

3. It has been said, "Love is a choice." Is infatuation ever a choice? Explain.

4. Of the first four tests — time, knowledge, focus, and singularity — which one is most important to you?

5. In your most important relationships, to what degree is your attention focused on what you are receiving from them and to what degree is your attention focused on meeting the other's needs?

Before You "Fall in Love"

SESSION 3 KEYS

● Love is different than infatuation.

● True love is distinguished from infatuation by time, knowledge, focus, and singularity.

ACTION STEPS

For anyone who intends to be romantically involved, it is crucial to understand the difference between love and infatuation. Both can involve such strong emotions that your thinking can become cloudy. How will you tell them apart in your life? In the space below, describe some basic characteristics that you can use to distinguish love from infatuation in the future.

Before You "Fall in Love"

AT HOME

As Proverbs 5:19 demonstrates, it's possible to be infatuated AND be in love. However, infatuation makes it harder to tell if love is the real thing. We've said that true love is distinguished by time, knowledge, focus, and singularity. In the spaces below, create your own criteria that must be met when the real thing comes along.

MY STANDARDS FOR:

Time

Knowledge

Focus

Singularity

MEMORY VERSE

> Let her affection fill you at all times with delight,
> be infatuated always with her love....
> Why should you be infatuated, my son, with a
> loose woman and embrace the bosom of an
> adventuress?
> ~ Proverbs 5:19-20 (NRSV)

How to Know If You're in Love

INTRODUCTION

As we've already discovered, infatuation is often mistaken for love. But they're not the same. Infatuation is a temporary attraction that is driven predominantly by feelings and physical characteristics. Love is an enduring affection driven by a mature, spiritual choice to be a vessel, sharing God's love with another person.

In this session, we'll explore in deeper detail the different sides of true love. Love has the potential to create many feelings. But many times, love is simply a choice. And sooner or later, we will all face situations where we are called to give love even though the person doesn't deserve it.

How to Know If You're in Love

Video Notes

IS IT LOVE OR INFATUATION?

Test # 5 - __Security__

An individual in love tends to have a sense of security and a feeling of trust after considering everything involved in his relationship with the other person. An infatuated individual tends to have a blind sense of security based upon wishful thinking rather than upon careful consideration, or he may have a sense of insecurity that is sometimes expressed as jealousy.

Test # 6 - __Work__

An individual in love works for the other person or for their mutual benefit. He may study to make the other person proud of him. His ambition is spurred and he plans and saves for the future. He may daydream, but his dreams are reasonably attainable. An infatuated person may lose his ambition, his appetite, his interest in everyday affairs.

How to Know If You're in Love

Test # 7- _Problem Solving_

A couple in love faces problems frankly and attempts to solve them. If there are barriers to their getting married, these barriers are approached intelligently and removed or circumvented. In infatuation, problems tend to be disregarded or glossed over.

Test # 8- _Distance_

Love tends to be constant. Infatuation often varies with the distance between the couple.

Test # 9- _Physical attraction & Involvement_

Physical attraction is a relatively smaller part of their total relationship when a couple is in love, a relatively greater part when they are infatuated. When a couple is in love, any physical contact they have tends to have meaning as well as be a pleasurable experience in and of itself. It tends to express what they feel toward each other. In infatuation, physical contact tends to be an end in itself. It represents only pleasurable experience devoid of meaning.

How to Know If You're in Love

Test # 10- _Affection_

In love, an expression of affection tends to come relatively late in the couple's relationship. In infatuation, it may come earlier, sometimes from the very beginning. _2 Samuel 13_

Test # 11- _Stability_

Love tends to endure.
Infatuation may change suddenly, unpredictably.

Test # 12- _Delayed Gratification_

A couple in love is not indifferent to the effects of postponement of their wedding and do not prolong the period of postponement unless they find it wiser to wait a reasonable time; they do not feel an almost irresistible drive toward haste. Infatuated couples tend to feel an urge toward getting married. Postponement is intolerable to them and they interpret it as deprivation rather than preparation.

Adapted from _Marriage for Moderns_ by Dr. Henry Bowman

How to Know If You're in Love

HOW TO DEVELOP YOUR LOVE LIFE

A Picture of Love

Eros
Lovers - erotic

Phileo
(Companionship & friends)

Love

Agape
(brothers + sisters)
doing what choose right b/c are not b/c what feel

A Word to Singles & Involved Couples…

1. Keep your _emotional_ and _physical_
   involvement behind your leading from God and
   commitment to the other person.

Hold off on letting your emotions run wild There
is a way to do rel w/o bring all the baggage

A Word to Married Couples…

2. Love requires the nourishment of all three kinds of
   love. Examine which one _your_ _mate_
   needs most and choose to give it as an act of
   worship to God.

> *"Absence diminishes small loves*
> *and increases great ones, as the wind blows*
> *out the candle and fans the bonfire."*
> *~ François Duc de La Rochefoucauld*

How to Know If You're in Love

Discussion Questions

1. In the test between love and infatuation, what did you learn about your previous or current relationship? If you identified your relationship as infatuation, which criteria was most helpful?

2. In the pyramid picture of love, which of the three types of love do you think is most important to a marriage? Explain.

3. The three types of love must be in balance for a healthy and lasting relationship. Is there a type of love that has been out of balance in your previous or current relationship?

4. Why is it important to recognize which kind of love the other person needs?

5. A *question for the single*:
   What are some ways you can keep your emotional and physical involvement "behind God's leading"?

   A *question for the married*:
   What is one thing you can do this week that will communicate to your spouse the kind of love that he or she needs?

How to Know If You're in Love

- Love is different from infatuation.

- The three types of love must be in balance for a lasting relationship.

- Your emotional and physical involvement must not surpass God's leading for your relationship.

ACTION STEPS

If you are single, briefly describe your plan to keep your emotional and physical involvement from getting ahead of God's leading in your relationship. Once you have a plan, identify a form of accountability that you can put into practice so that your plan will be successful.

If you are married, identify in the space below which of the three types of love your spouse most needs from you at this time. Describe your plans to give that love this week. At the end of the week, evaluate your success. Then spend time in discussion with your spouse on how to make this a lasting change in your relationship.

How to Know If You're in Love

AT HOME

Read 2 Samuel 13:1-15.

In verse 15, how would you explain the sudden shift of Amnon's feelings toward Tamar?

Which kind of love had Amnon felt toward her?

MEMORY VERSE

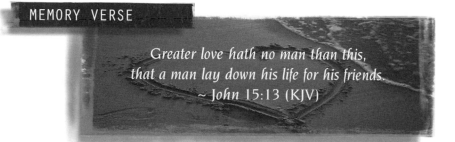

*Greater love hath no man than this,
that a man lay down his life for his friends.*
~ John 15:13 (KJV)

Love and Sex: Knowing the Difference Makes All the Difference

INTRODUCTION

Sexual dissatisfaction is one of the fastest growing concerns among married people today. Despite all their dreams of great sex during their married years, many couples consider their sex lives to be a major let-down. Some blame it on poor technique, physical inadequacy, or a lack of interest. But for most of these couples, their sexual disappointment can be traced back to a basic misunderstanding of the relationship between love and sex.

Increasingly today, love and sex are portrayed synonymously. In an effort to experience love, many people destroy the thing that was meant to communicate it at the deepest level. If we truly understood the difference between love and sex, it would change our whole perspective on dating and marriage.

17% of women actually plan to have sex the first time they have intercourse

Video Notes

A SEA OF DISTORTIONS - FOUR PEOPLE'S STORIES:

Lauren —

Mike —

Paula counseling a woman in her 20s —

Paula counseling a woman in her 30s —

Love and Sex:
Knowing the Difference
Makes All the Difference

The Lie:
Sex is necessary to keep a growing relationship alive.

THE TRUTH:

Once sex enters into a relationship, it almost always disintegrates instead of getting better.

The Lie:

If we really love each other, sex is sanctified.

THE TRUTH:

Sex is sanctified only inside the union of biblical marriage.

The Lie:
Having sex is a rite of passage.

THE TRUTH:

With every sexual encounter you diminish the possibility and capacity to experience true intimacy.

THE COMMON THREAD:

They didn't understand the _difference_ between love and sex.

SUMMARY:

When we fail to understand the difference between love and sex, we are doomed to failure in both our _relationships_ and our _sexuality_.

Eph 5:3

> "What is commonly called love, namely the desire
> of satisfying a voracious appetite with a certain
> quantity of delicate white human flesh."
> ~Henry Fielding

> "I know nothing about sex,
> because I was always married."
> ~Zsa Zsa Gabor

Discussion Questions

1. There were four stories shared during the video segment.
   What are some of the lies the individuals believed about sex?

2. Of all the lies described, which one have you come the closest to
   believing in your life? If you have bought into the lie, how has it
   impacted your life?

3. How would knowing the difference between love and sex have
   changed the outcomes for:
   Lauren?

   Mike?

   Woman in her 20s?

   Woman in her 30s?

4. How can physical intimacy outside of marriage seem so appealing
   in one moment and cause such pain later on?

5. Chip tells us that sex apart from total commitment (marriage) pro-
   duces spiritual seperation. What does he mean by this?

Love and Sex: Knowing the Difference Makes All the Difference

SESSION 5 KEYS

● Distorted thinking usually feels "right" before it makes things go wrong.

● When we fail to understand the difference between love and sex, we are doomed to failure in both our relationships and our sexuality.

ACTION STEPS

It's important to know where you stand on such important issues as love and sex. The crucial decisions in life are never made in the heat of battle. In the space below, describe your beliefs about love and sex, including the standards you intend to uphold in your life.

Love and Sex: Knowing the Difference Makes All the Difference

AT HOME

This week, pay attention to the messages around you - on television, the radio, in the movies, and in conversations at work or with friends. Do you hear any distortions being repeated or reinforced? In the space below, briefly describe some of the attitudes and beliefs that are commonly portrayed in your world. Be prepared to share your findings with the group.

MEMORY VERSE

Flee from sexual immorality.
All other sins a man commits are outside his body, but
he who sins sexually sins against his own body.
~ 1 Corinthians 6:18-19 (NIV)

The Difference Between Love and Sex

INTRODUCTION

There's a profound paradox about sex. It was created to be the ultimate expression of love; and yet, if mishandled, it has the potential to be the ultimate expression of disrespect, selfishness, and degradation. Sex itself is a form of deep, spiritual communication. And it always conveys one of these two, distinctly different messages. It all depends on the context in which it happens.

Your future fulfillment as a sexual being hinges on your understanding of the message sex communicates between you and your partner. Will it be a deep expression of mutual devotion and commitment? Or is it possible that sex, although pleasurable, could be telling your partner that he or she isn't that special at all?

The Difference Between Love and Sex

Video Notes

THE CONTEXT

God's Concern for Our Relationships

> [30]And do not grieve the Holy Spirit of God, by whom you were sealed for the day of redemption. [31]Let all bitterness and wrath and anger and clamor and slander be put away from you, along with all malice. [32]And be kind to one another, tender-hearted, forgiving each other, just as God in Christ also has forgiven you.
> ~ Ephesians 4:30-32 (NASB)

THE COMMAND

Walk in Love!

How?

1. **Positively** - Be giving, caring, sacrificial, and unselfish toward others.

   > [1]Therefore be imitators of God, as beloved children; [2]and walk in love, just as Christ also loved you, and gave Himself up for us, an offering and a sacrifice to God as a fragrant aroma. ~ Ephesians 5:1-2 (NASB)

2. **Negatively** - Refuse to take, exploit, cheapen, defraud, or substitute sexual activity for genuine love and authentic intimacy.

   > [3]But do not let immorality or any impurity or greed even be named among you, as is proper among saints; [4]and no filthiness, silly talk, coarse jesting, which are not fitting, but rather giving of thanks. ~ Ephesians 5:3-4 (NASB)

The Difference Between Love and Sex

THE REASON

Sexual Impurity Destroys Relationships

5For this you know with certainty, that no immoral or impure person or covetous man, (who is an idolater), has an inheritance in the kingdom of Christ and God. 6Let no one deceive you with empty words, for because of these things (mentioned above) the wrath of God comes upon the sons of disobedience. ~ **Ephesians 5:5-6 (NASB)**

SPECIFIC APPLICATION

To uninvolved singles: Develop the personal _____ to pursue purity.

To involved singles: Develop a _____ to adopt standards of purity.

To people in crisis: Get _____.

To married people: _____ about it.

To all: "Come now, let us _____ together," says the LORD. "Though your sins are like scarlet, they shall be as white as snow; though they are red as crimson, they shall be like wool." ~ Isaiah 1:18 (NIV)

"There is nothing like early promiscuous sex for dispelling life's bright mysterious expectations."
~Iris Murdoch

Discussion Questions

1. What does obeying and trusting God in the arena of love and sex look like in your life?

2. How would you define sexual immorality? Why is it impossible to be sexually immoral and grow in your relationship with Christ?

3. Why is sex outside of God's boundaries unloving and destructive in relationships?

4. Why is sexual purity so important to God? What steps will you take towards sexual purity in the coming week?

5. Read Isaiah 1:18. What does it say about God's love and plans for us?

SESSION 6

The Difference Between Love and Sex

SESSION 6 KEYS

● Sex can either communicate love, or it can communicate disrespect, selfishness, and degradation.

● Sexual immorality destroys relationships.

● Sexual immorality is idolatry-worship of self, not God.

ACTION STEPS

From the video notes, which of the Specific Application points most applies to your situation? In the space below, briefly describe how you will take the prescribed action this week.

The Difference Between Love and Sex

AT HOME

Sometimes it's hard to believe that God would reserve sex for marriage while not approving it for unmarried couples who truly love each other. Does it really matter that much? Is there something magical about the wedding ceremony … or the marriage license? This week, read Ephesians 5:1-6 again on your own. Then in the space below, write your own explanation of how sex should relate to love and marriage.

MEMORY VERSE

But immorality or any impurity or greed must not even be named among you, as is proper among saints;
~ Ephesians 5:3 (NASB)

Sexual Purity in a Sex-Saturated World

INTRODUCTION

The pull of sex is one of the strongest forces in nature. In fact, statistics show that sexual immorality is virtually the same between church-going and unchurched groups. Despite the fact that they believe it's wrong, many people who consider themselves Christians are powerless when it comes to resisting the intoxicating power of sex.

The same is true for you. Even if you have a desire to pursue sexual purity for your life, that's not enough. Despite your intentions and your sincerity, you need something more if it is to become a reality.

Sexual Purity in a Sex-Saturated World

Video Notes

FIVE FACTS ABOUT SEX

1. Those who abstain from sexual intercourse before marriage report the _____ levels of sexual satisfaction in marriage.

2. Those who cohabitate before marriage have a 50% higher rate of _____ than those who do not.

3. Those who cohabitate are more likely to experience _____ in marriage.

4. The introduction of sex into a dating relationship almost always ushers in the _____ of the relationship.

5. Sexually-transmitted diseases, including AIDS, can remain _____ for up to a decade or more but can be passed on to others during that time.

HOW TO SAY "YES" TO LOVE AND "NO" TO SECOND-RATE SEX

I. Loving relationships demand sexual _____.

THE COMMAND

Refrain from sexual immorality.

> [2] and walk in love, just as Christ also loved you and gave Himself up for us, an offering and a sacrifice to God as a fragrant aroma. [3] But immorality or any impurity or greed must not even be named among you, as is proper among saints; [4] and there must be no filthiness and silly talk, or coarse jesting, which are not fitting, but rather giving of thanks.
> ~ Ephesians 5:2-4 (NASB)

Sexual Purity in a Sex-Saturated World

THE REASON

He (God) loves you.

⁵For this you know with certainty, that no immoral or impure person or covetous man, who is an idolater, has an inheritance in the kingdom of Christ and God. ⁶Let no one deceive you with empty words, for because of these things the wrath of God comes upon the sons of disobedience. ~ Ephesians 5:5-6 (NASB)

THE APPLICATION

Do not participate in sin, for you are brand-new in Christ.

⁷Therefore do not be partakers with them; ⁸for you were formerly darkness, but now you are Light in the Lord; walk as children of Light ⁹(for the fruit of the Light consists in all **goodness** and **righteousness** and **truth**), ¹⁰trying to learn what is pleasing to the Lord. ~ Ephesians 5:7-10 (NASB)

HOW TO SAY "YES" TO LOVE AND "NO" TO SECOND-RATE SEX

I. Loving relationships demand sexual purity.

II. Sexual purity demands a game plan.

(to be continued...)

"Whoever is in a hurry shows
that the thing he is about is too big for him."
~ Lord Chesterfield

Sexual Purity in a Sex-Saturated World

Discussion Questions

1. Does the fact that premarital and extramarital sex are "taboo" make them more appealing? Why or why not?

2. What are some examples of rules that you're glad exist?

3. Why do you think the idea of delayed gratification motivates some people but not others?

4. Outside of marriage, how far is "too far"? Why?

5. Which of God's rules about sex feels the most restricting to you? Why?

Sexual Purity in a Sex-Saturated World

SESSION 7 KEYS

● Every gift that flows out of love almost always comes with rules.

● God's rules for sex always maximize our pleasure in the long run.

● Loving relationships demand sexual purity.

ACTION STEPS

Read Ephesians 5:7-12. According to this passage, how far should you go to ensure that you are not a "partaker" of immorality? What would this look like in your life? After reading the Scripture and pondering the questions, spend some time in prayer. Ask God to show the appropriate boundaries for your relationships (current or future). Be prepared to share your boundaries with a trusted friend or accountability partner.

Sexual Purity in a Sex-Saturated World

AT HOME

The purpose of God's rules about sex is to maximize your relationships in the future. Read Romans 12:2. What is one thing you can do now to take a step toward greater purity and maximize your relationships?

MEMORY VERSE

Therefore do not be partakers with them; for you were formerly darkness, but now you are Light in the Lord; walk as children of Light (for the fruit of the Light consists in all **goodness** and **righteousness** and **truth**), trying to learn what is pleasing to the Lord.
~ Ephesians 5:7-10 (NASB)

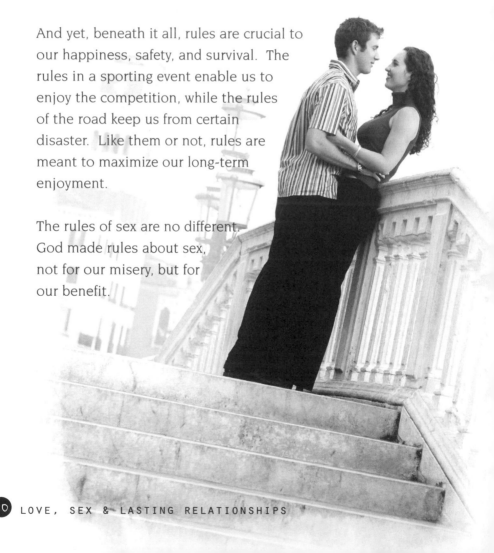

How to Say "Yes" to Love and "No" to Second-Rate Sex

INTRODUCTION

There's something about rules that seems to take the fun out of everything. Since the time of Adam and Eve, men and women have had a hard time accepting rules without testing them first. When something is off limits, somehow it becomes all the more attractive to the human spirit.

And yet, beneath it all, rules are crucial to our happiness, safety, and survival. The rules in a sporting event enable us to enjoy the competition, while the rules of the road keep us from certain disaster. Like them or not, rules are meant to maximize our long-term enjoyment.

The rules of sex are no different. God made rules about sex, not for our misery, but for our benefit.

Video Notes

HOW TO SAY "YES" TO LOVE AND "NO" TO SECOND-RATE SEX

I. Loving relationships demand sexual _____.

II. Sexual purity demands a _____ _____.

    1. Develop _____
       Purity requires a personal commitment to the truth.
       (Ephesians 5:2-4)

    2. Ponder the _____.
       Fear can be a legitimate and healthy motivator for delayed
       gratification. (Ephesians 5:5-6)

    3. Make _____.
       Advanced decision making is an absolute necessity for
       sexual purity. (Ephesians 5:7-9)

    4. Get _____.
       Asking others to help you keep your commitments to God
       will empower you to walk "pleasing to the Lord."
       (Ephesians 5:10)

> *And do not be conformed to this world, but be transformed by
> the renewing of your mind, so that you may prove what the will
> of God is, that which is good and acceptable and perfect. ~*
> **Romans 12:2 (NASB)**

III. Sexual Purity's Pay Off is Awesome!

    1. God's way _____!

    2. It's never too _____!

    3. A word to virgins: you are not _____,
       you are wise!

> "What matters is not the idea a man holds,
> but the depth at which he holds it."
> ~ Ezra Pound

Discussion Questions

1. In your own words, what is the difference between belief and conviction? In what areas of your life do you need to convert your beliefs to convictions?

2. How can fear be a legitimate and healthy motivator for sexual purity?

3. How does your perception of a person change after learning that he or she is a virgin?

4. What specific pre-decisions are you going to make to help you win your battle for sexual purity?

5. Who is the person that can help you develop a game plan and hold you accountable to your commitment to God? What would your game plan need to include?

How to Say "Yes" to Love and "No" to Second-Rate Sex

SESSION 8 KEYS

● Sexual purity demands a game plan.

● Get accountability!

● It's never too late to become sexually pure.

ACTION STEPS

Take Chip up on his challenge. Spend some time alone with God this week. Seek His guidance as you determine your personal convictions for staying sexually pure.
Then take a moment to ponder the consequences.
Finally, make a list of your pre-decisions.

AT HOME

Accountability is perhaps the most important key to success against temptation. It can also be one of the most intimidating to pursue. This week, prayerfully consider sharing your list of pre-decisions with one or two trustworthy believers. Even if your attempts to reach out feel a bit awkward, the rewards can be priceless!

MEMORY VERSE

Run from anything that gives you the evil thoughts that young men often have, but stay close to anything that makes you want to do right. Have faith and love, and enjoy the companionship of those who love the Lord and have pure hearts.
~ 2 Timothy 2:22 (TLB)

Wake Up World! There's a Better Way to Do Relationships

INTRODUCTION

Hollywood suggests that successful relationships are built on finding the right person, falling in love, and fixing your hopes and dreams of future fulfillment on that person. But relationships aren't working, marriages are failing, and we're left wondering "Why?"

Something is wrong.
So where do we turn for answers to this complex issue?

God has given us a revolutionary way to build relationships with the opposite sex — a way that honors the other person, a way built on love, a way that results in deeper intimacy and long-term commitment.

Wake Up World! There's a Better Way to Do Relationships

Video Notes

CHIP'S STORY

"A Norman Rockwell Picture"

27 years ago… A small farmhouse in the country…A young couple beginning God's journey together… An ordinary moment with extraordinary impact…

A "_____" that changed my life

CHIP'S REALIZATION

"God sets boundaries because He wants to give you His very best."

*He who did not spare his own Son, but gave him up for us all-how will he not also, along with him, graciously give us all things? ~ **Romans** 8:32 (NIV)*

CHIP'S EPIPHANY

"I am going to do life God's way."

*Where there is no revelation, the people cast off restraint; but blessed is he who keeps the law. ~ **Proverbs** 29:18 (NIV)*

Wake Up World! There's a Better Way to Do Relationships

WHY IS SEX SUCH SERIOUS BUSINESS TO GOD?

Ephesians 5:11-14

The Command =

> *And do not participate in the unfruitful deeds of darkness,*
> *but instead even expose them;*
> *verse 11*

The Reason =

> *. . . for it is disgraceful even to speak of the things*
> *which are done by them in secret.*
> *verse 12*

The Explanation =

> *But all things become visible when they are exposed by the light,*
> *for everything that becomes visible is light.*
> *verse 13*

The Invitation =

> *For this reason it says, 'Awake, sleeper, and arise from the dead,*
> *and Christ will shine on you.'*
> *verse 14*

"The soul never thinks without a picture."
~ Aristotle

Wake Up World! There's a Better Way to Do Relationships

SESSION 9

Discussion Questions

1. Why is sex such serious business to God? What is at stake for the world around us?

2. Chip described the time he got a vision for the type of family life he wanted. Describe your vision for the family and relationship you've always dreamed of.

3. Sexual immorality so violates God's holy character that He tells us not to even speak about it. What does Chip suggest is more powerful than our words?

4. What does Chip mean when he says that your life is a "light"? How can you be an ambassador to pass it on?

5. What would happen if God's church said, "Let's get radical!"? What changes would you need to make in your life to be part of the "second sexual revolution"?

Wake Up World! There's a Better Way to Do Relationships

SESSION 9 KEYS

● Sex is serious business to God.

● We are to expose the world's destructive attitude toward sex, not by what we say, but by how we live.

ACTION STEPS

Set aside some time this week and rate yourself on scale of one to ten. How would you rank your own sexual purity in mind, word, and deed? Write a sentence or two to explain your answer for each.

Wake Up World! There's a Better Way to Do Relationships

AT HOME

Remembering that night in a little farmhouse, Chip basked in the glow of a pure and loving relationship and for the first time saw sexual purity the way God sees it. The light exposed his distorted view of sex and his twisted view of relationships. In that defining moment Chip decided "I'm going to live my life God's way."

Have you ever had a moment like that where God spoke into your life so clearly? Take some time this week and evaluate the defining moments of your life. How did you respond to the call to change?

MEMORY VERSE

Where there is no revelation,
the people cast off restraint;
but blessed is he who keeps the law.
~ Proverbs 29:18 (NASB)

The Second Sexual Revolution

INTRODUCTION

Great ideas can spread like wildfire. And all it takes to get it started is a spark.

God's ideas about sex are great ideas. Can you imagine a world dominated by the truth about sex? What if TV, music, and the movies no longer repeated distortions about sex and relationships? What if they began to reflect God's view instead?

It's possible. All it takes is a very small percentage of faithful people who are serious about doing sex God's way.

The Second Sexual Revolution

Video Notes

ANATOMY OF A SEXUAL REVOLUTION

I. A revolutionary way to _____ about human sexuality.

    1. Sex is _____ —

    2. Sex is _____ —

[15]Do you not know that your bodies are members of Christ? Shall I then take away the members of Christ and make them members of a prostitute? May it never be! [16]Or do you not know that the one who joins himself to a prostitute is one body with her? For He says, "THE TWO SHALL BECOME ONE FLESH." [17]But the one who joins himself to the Lord is one spirit with Him. [18]Flee immorality. Every other sin that a man commits is outside the body, but the immoral man sins against his own body. [19]Or do you not know that your body is a temple of the Holy Spirit who is in you, whom you have from God, and that you are not your own? [20]For you have been bought with a price: therefore glorify God in your body. ~ 1 **Corinthians** 6:15-20 **(NASB)**

*Marriage is to be held in honor among all, and the marriage bed is to be undefiled; for fornicators and adulterers God will judge. ~ **Hebrews** 13:4 **(NASB)***

II. A revolutionary way to _____ the opposite sex.

[3]*Your adornment must not be merely external-braiding the hair, and wearing gold jewelry, or putting on dresses; [4]but let it be the hidden person of the heart, with the imperishable quality of a gentle and quiet spirit, which is precious in the sight of God. ~1* **Peter** 3:3-4 **(NASB)**

I _____ Character

O _____ Modesty

U _____ Devotion

III. A revolutionary way to _____ to the opposite sex.

    1. As a _____.

> Greater love has no one than this, that one lay down his life for his friends.
> ~ John 15:13 (NASB)

    2. As a _____ member.

> [1]Do not sharply rebuke an older man, but rather appeal to him as a father, to the younger men as brothers, [2]the older women as mothers, and the younger women as sisters, in all purity. ~1 Timothy 5:1-2 (NASB)

    3. As fellow _____ ____ _____.

> [24]and let us consider how to stimulate one another to love and good deeds, [25]not forsaking our own assembling together, as is the habit of some, but encouraging one another; and all the more as you see the day drawing near.
> ~ Hebrews 10:24-25 (NASB)

> "Revolutions are not made: they come.
> A revolution is as natural as an oak tree.
> It comes out of the past;
> its foundations are laid far back."
> ~ Wendell Phillips

The Second Sexual Revolution

Discussion Questions

1. Is the time right to start a revolution? Why or why not?
   In your opinion, what does it take to start a revolution?

2. In what ways do you need to change how you think about sex?
   What implications does this have on your thought life? Behavior?
   Viewing habits? Renewing of your mind?

3. How does modesty facilitate loving and lasting relationships?
   In what ways has our culture seduced us into attracting the
   opposite sex in ways that focus on outer versus inner qualities?

4. Is it possible that the whole "dating paradigm" is not the wisest or
   most effective way to build relationships with the opposite sex?
   Explain.

5. How could you answer God's call to the "Second Sexual
   Revolution"? What might that look like in your life and
   relationships?

The Second Sexual Revolution

SESSION 10 KEYS

● Revolution means a new way to think about human sexuality.

● Revolution means a new way to attract the opposite sex.

● Revolution means a new way to relate to the opposite sex.

ACTION STEPS

This week, start a personal revolution by committing to a new approach to the opposite sex. In the spaces below, describe how you will think about, attract, and relate to the opposite sex. Give specific examples for each.

THINK ABOUT:

ATTRACT:

RELATE TO:

The Second Sexual Revolution

AT HOME

Are you ready to take a radical step of faith and believe God's Word that:

1. Sex is sacred
2. Sex is serious
3. Sex is an awesome responsibility

In what specific ways do you need to change your way of thinking in order to become part of the second sexual revolution?

We need a countercultural movement among Christians to let God's light shine. After you've spent some time in the Word and in prayer, I encourage you to put what you've experienced in the last 10 sessions in to practice. Turn the page, follow the outline, and make a personal covenant with your Father. He loves you, He's for you, and He wants to give you His best. I invite you to join me in answering God's call to a second sexual revolution!

MEMORY VERSE

And let not your adornment be merely external- braiding the hair, and wearing gold jewelry, or putting on dresses; but let it be the hidden person of the heart, with the imperishable quality of a gentle and quiet spirit, which is precious in the sight of God.
~ 1 Peter 3:3-4 (NASB)

Heavenly Father,

Thank you for your Word in Ephesians that teaches me how to love as you would have me to do so. Thank you that the same power that raised Christ from the dead lives in me and enables me to be pure. Help me to think differently about my sexuality, to attract others with integrity and honesty, and to relate in truthful and helpful ways to those around me.

From this day forward I will be sexually pure. Give me your strength to become the right person, to grow and walk in love, and to fix my hope on you, walking in your light. Give me the courage to be radical in my faith and allow me to make a difference as I commit to be a part of the second sexual revolution.

Amen.

My pre-decisions for sexual purity are:

1.

2.

3.

My game plan for sexual purity is:

1.

2.

3.

My accountability partners are:

1.

2.

I want to become a part of the second sexual revolution
and choose not simply to talk about my faith, but to live it out.

_____   _____
Name   Date

Welcome to the Revolution

by Chip Ingram

Dear Friends,

As the old song says "It only takes a spark to get a fire going" and the fact of the matter is, it's true! So how about you? Are you ready for the second sexual revolution? Will you join me?

Learning this material may be a great first step, but revolutions occur when there is a movement. Movements occur when people go beyond themselves and become committed to taking it to the next level of impact.

My question for you, as you finish this series is: "*How will you take what you've learned in this series and "pass it on" to your circle of influence?*"

Many people have already completed *Love, Sex & Lasting Relationships* and have now launched it successfully in their high school, college, single's group, or small groups in their church.

I encourage you to share what you've learned with those in your network of friends. If you have a testimony of how this study has impacted your life, I'd love to hear from you. You can email me at info@lote.org.

Keep Pressin' Ahead,

Leading Your Group Through Love, Sex and Lasting Relationships

THE TOOLS FOR THIS SERIES

Living on the Edge has prepared a comprehensive course to bring the principles of this series alive in each participant's life. Your job is to guide your group through the study sessions and the exercises, allowing them to discover the concepts, embrace their meaning, and apply them to their lives.

Love, Sex & Lasting Relationships is intended to be more than just a course. It is a 10-week experience that will equip the people in your group to experience God's design for intimacy with the opposite sex. This kit contains:

Ten **Video** sessions featuring the teaching of Chip Ingram.

A **Study Guide** designed to help each participant personalize the lessons. Complete with: Video Notes with a fill-in-the-blank outline for taking notes during each of the video sessions; penetrating Group Discussion Questions that correspond with each lesson; and life-changing exercises to implement the lessons into everyday life.

The video sessions and the study guide are designed to create a learning experience that equips participants not only to understand God's design for relationships, but also to begin applying those principles right away. (To order extra materials for *Love, Sex & Lasting Relationships*, log on www.lote.org.

Leading Your Group Through Love, Sex and Lasting Relationships

GETTING STARTED - 4 EASY STEPS

Several basic ingredients are essential to any successful group study. Before you plan the first meeting, you should work through these fundamentals.

1. First, pray! Only God can change the hearts of men, and prayer is your most powerful tool. As the leader of your group, this is your logical starting place.

2. Next, organize. Consider asking one or two others to share the leadership load by helping you plan, promote the series, distribute materials, etc.

3. Order the Study Guide. Before starting the course, make sure that each participant has his own copy of the Study Guide. You may want to have extra copies on hand to accommodate any late additions to your group. This series is designed to be highly interactive, and the Study Guide is essential for integrating the principles into daily life.

   (If your sponsoring organization is not underwriting the cost of materials, then consider structuring your class so that the Study Guide is part of a registration fee for the series.)

4. Prepare to lead the sessions. In the following pages of this Leader's Guide, you will find a Session Guide for each of the ten Video Sessions. Each one contains guidelines for the class, discussion questions, and tips. You can keep the Session Guide with you during your group time, to help you lead each session with confidence!

Things to Remember While Leading This Series

TRIED AND TRUE TIPS FOR THE SUCCESSFUL VIDEO SERIES LEADER

● **Cover The Material:**

Of all the things you do as the leader of this series, your main objective is to work through each Video Session and cover the discussion questions with your group in the allotted time. Each of the ten video lessons is accompanied by important discussion questions, exercises, and Scriptures. There's a lot of searching and growing to be done between lessons, and it all builds on the content of the video and the discussion questions. It is STRONGLY RECOMMENDED that you view one session at a time, in order for the rest of the materials to have their full effect.

● **Let The Teacher Teach:**

Chip Ingram is the "expert" in this series. For over nearly thirty years he has been studying scripture, counseling, and exploring the issues surrounding love and sex in relationships. Since he brings his expertise to every session, you can sit back and relax while he presents the material. Your expertise is needed in facilitating his teaching and cultivating good conversation during the discussion time. The Leader's Guide and the Study Guide will prove to be helpful for you as the facilitator.

● **Be Yourself:**

The others in your group will appreciate and follow your example of openness and honesty as you lead - so set a good example! The best way to encourage those in your class is not to impress them with your own wisdom, but with your sincere desire to live out these principles in your own life. When they sense that you are "real" - that you are not "above" the issues that challenge them - they will be encouraged to press on. Someone who struggles with sexual purity needs encouragement to overcome the challenges. The transparency of your group may be the crucial ingredient that sparks their motivation.

Things to Remember While Leading This Series

● Be Prepared:

Hopefully, the discussion questions will raise some interesting conversation in your group. However, you can also lose focus during discussion time as people present opinions that may detract from the focus of the lesson, or may not represent biblical teaching. A good way to keep things on track is to point the conversation back to a related point that is covered in the *Love, Sex, and Lasting Relationships* materials. But that can only happen if you are familiar with the lessons. If you will be the leader throughout the entire series, Living on the Edge recommends that you view all of the video sessions before beginning your series. If the participants will be taking turns leading each week, this is not necessary. In many cases, your familiarity with the series content can help you keep things headed in the desired direction at all times.

ABOUT YOUR VIDEO TEACHER

Chip Ingram is your teacher for *Love, Sex, and Lasting Relationships*. Chip Ingram is the President and Teaching Pastor of Living on the Edge. Chip's successful radio program, which began in 1995, has expanded to over 900 stations nationwide. A graduate of Dallas Theological Seminary, Chip has a unique ability to communicate biblical truth in a way that brings about transformation in lives. He is also the father of four grown children.

Things to Remember While Leading This Series

HOW TO STRUCTURE YOUR GROUP TIME

Whether you are leading this series in Sunday School or a small group Bible Study, you'll find the materials are ideal for most small group settings. The course is designed so that the video teaching and the discussion questions will fit into an hour segment. Of course, you can take extra time for discussion or to review the previous week's material if time permits. Whatever your time frame, be sure that your group views one new video lesson per week, and that they complete their homework assignments between meetings.

Below is the suggested way to use these materials.

IN CLASS

1. *Video Class Notes:*

   Each video session has a corresponding section in the Study Guide for participants to follow along as Chip teaches. A numbered, fill-in-the-blank outline highlights the main points of the video, and there is room for additional notes and insights as well. The "answers" to the notes can be found in this Leader's Guide for each session.

2. *Discussion Questions:*

   The Study Guide also contains discussion questions for each of the video sessions. They are designed to help your participants personalize the content of each lesson. You can move right to these questions immediately after the conclusion of the video.

   VERY IMPORTANT: The main goal of these questions is to help you stir up discussion in your group. Encourage your group to answer with more than short "yes" and "no" answers. Use the questions to draw people into discussing their hearts, their struggles, and how the teaching could be applied to their personal situations.

3. *Action Steps:*

The Study Guide then moves into specific action steps that are designed to help create specific ways to apply the material. Your group will benefit tremendously by sharing ideas and discussing the recommended action steps together. Some of the best discussion time comes from this segment. Be sure to be honest and transparent during this time. Make it clear that you are a fellow learner, not an untouchable "expert" on the Bible and relationships. Make your group a safe environment for sharing personal struggles. Together, your group can minister to each other, helping to apply God's word to everyday situations.

AFTER CLASS

4. *At Home:*

These in-depth, personal studies are intended to motivate the students to take the principles right off the page and into their lives. This is where the series moves from contemplation to application. As the participants immerse themselves in these materials each day, the transformation process begins. Urge the people in your group to complete their assignments weekly. Insist on it! You may even want to include a brief review of their home work at the designated point near the end of each week's group discussion.

SUGGESTED FORMAT

1. View the Video Lesson, filling in the notes in the Study Guide (25-35 minutes)

2. Review the Discussion Questions (20 minutes)

3. Clarify assignment for upcoming week (5 minutes)

4. Prayer requests, group prayer (10 minutes)

Leader's Guide Session Notes

SESSION 1

HOLLYWOOD'S FORMULA FOR LASTING RELATIONSHIPS

Video Notes
Answer Key:

I. HOLLYWOOD'S PRESCRIPTION FOR LASTING RELATIONSHIPS:

1. <u>FIND</u> the right person.
2. <u>FALL</u> in love.
3. <u>FIX</u> your hopes and dreams of future fulfillment on that person.
4. If <u>FAILURE</u> occurs, repeat steps 1, 2, and 3.

II. GOD'S PRESCRIPTION FOR LASTING RELATIONSHIPS:

1. <u>BECOME</u> the right person.
2. <u>WALK</u> in love.
3. <u>FIX</u> your hope on God and seek to please Him through this relationship.

Leader's Guide
Session Notes

SESSION 2

TWO MODELS FOR LASTING RELATIONSHIPS

Video Notes
Answer Key:

GOD'S PROCESS FOR FALLING IN LOVE

1. Ask: Is this person a committed <u>BELIEVER</u>?
2. Observe the person <u>SOCIALLY</u>.
3. Get to <u>KNOW</u> each other.
4. Keep your emotions behind <u>GOD'S</u> lead.
5. Come together <u>PHYSICALLY</u>.

Leader's Guide Session Notes

SESSION 3

SESSION 3

BEFORE YOU "FALL IN LOVE"

Video Notes
Answer Key:

AM I IN LOVE?

EROS – This is need love.
PHILEO _ This is friendship love.
AGAPE – This is giving love.

IS IT LOVE OR INFATUATION?

TEST # 1: TIME

TEST # 2: KNOWLEDGE

TEST # 3: FOCUS

TEST # 4: SINGULARITY

Leader's Guide Session Notes

HOW TO DEVELOP YOUR LOVE LIFE

1. Keep your <u>EMOTIONAL</u> and <u>PHYSICAL</u> involvement behind your leading from God and commitment to the other person.

2. Love requires the nourishment of all three kinds of love. Examine which one <u>YOUR</u> <u>MATE</u> needs most and choose to give it as an act of worship to God.

SESSION 5

LOVE AND SEX: KNOWING THE DIFFERENCE MAKES ALL THE DIFFERENCE

Video Notes
Answer Key:

THE COMMON THREAD

1. They didn't understand the <u>DIFFERENCE</u> between love and sex.

SUMMARY

2. When we fail to understand the difference between love and sex, we are doomed to failure in both our <u>RELATIONSHIPS</u> and our <u>SEXUALITY</u>.

 LOVE, SEX & LASTING RELATIONSHIPS

SESSION 6

THE DIFFERENCE BETWEEN LOVE AND SEX

Video Notes
Answer Key:

1. TO uninvolved singles:
    Develop the personal <u>CONVICTION</u> to pursue purity.

2. TO involved singles:
    Develop a <u>STRATEGY</u> to adopt standards of purity.

3. TO people in crisis:
    Get <u>HELP</u>.

4. TO married people:
    <u>TALK</u> about it.

5. TO ALL:
    "Come now, let us <u>REASON</u> together," says the LORD.
    "Though your sins are like scarlet, they shall be as white as
    the snow; though they are red as crimson, they shall be like
    wool." Isaiah 1:18 (NIV)

Leader's Guide Session Notes

SESSION 7

SEXUAL PURITY IN A SEX-SATURATED WORLD

Video Notes
Answer Key:

FIVE FACTS ABOUT SEX:

1. Those who abstain from sexual intercourse before marriage report the <u>HIGHEST</u> levels of sexual satisfaction in marriage.

2. Those who cohabitate before marriage have a 50% higher rate of <u>DIVORCE</u> than those who do not.

3. Those who cohabitate are more likely to experience <u>INFIDELITY</u> in marriage.

4. The introduction of sex into a dating relationship almost always ushers in the <u>BREAKUP</u> of the relationship.

5. Sexually-transmitted diseases, including <u>AIDS</u>, can remain <u>DORMANT</u> for up to a decade or more, but can be passed on to others during that time.

IS IT LOVE OR INFATUATION?

1. Loving relationships demand sexual <u>PURITY</u>.

SESSION 8

HOW TO SAY "YES" TO LOVE AND "NO" TO SECOND-RATE SEX

Video Notes

Answer Key:

HOW TO SAY "YES" TO LOVE
AND "NO" TO SECOND-RATE SEX:

II. Sexual purity demands a <u>GAME</u> <u>PLAN</u>.
    1. Develop <u>CONVICTIONS</u>.
    2. Ponder the <u>CONSEQUENCES</u>.
    3. Make <u>PRE-DECISIONS</u>.
    4. <u>ACCOUNTABILITY</u>.

III. Sexual purity's payoff is awesome!
    1. God's way <u>WORKS</u>!
    2. It's never <u>TOO</u> <u>LATE</u>!
    3. A word to virgins: you are not <u>WEIRD</u>, you are wise

SESSION 9

WAKE UP WORLD! THERE'S A BETTER WAY TO DO RELATIONSHIPS

Video Notes

There are no fill-in-the-blanks in this session

Leader's Guide
Session Notes

SESSION 10

THE SECOND SEXUAL REVOLUTION

Video Notes
Answer Key:

ANATOMY OF A SEXUAL REVOLUTION:

I. A revolutionary way to <u>THINK</u> about human sexuality.

II. A revolutionary way to <u>ATTRACT</u> the opposite sex.

      1. Sex is <u>SACRED</u>

      2. Sex is <u>SERIOUS</u>

            1. <u>INWARD</u> Character

            2. <u>OUTWARD</u> Modesty

            3. <u>UPWARD</u> Devotion

III. A revolutionary way to <u>RELATE</u> to the opposite sex.

      1. As a <u>FRIEND</u>.

      2. As a <u>FAMILY</u> member.

      3. As fellow <u>FOLLOWER</u> <u>OF</u> <u>CHRIST</u>.

Infatuation not bad, but we cannot fund our relationship
on infatuation.

Infatuation isn't bad, it takes us too deep too early

What's Next?

Small Group Studies offered by Chip Ingram and Living on the Edge.

GOD: AS HE LONGS FOR YOU TO SEE HIM

How would you describe God? Awesome? All Powerful? Creator? While we cannot know Him exhaustively, we can know Him truly. And God longs for you to see Him as He truly is. Join Chip in this fascinating series studying the seven attributes of God.

MIRACLE OF LIFE CHANGE

Is life change really possible? If we're honest most of us would answer, "No." You've tried numerous programs that promise big changes, but in reality, deliver very little results. You long for transformation, but don't know where to begin. There's good news for you and there is hope. Life change is possible!

r12: LIVING ON THE EDGE

Being a genuine disciple of Christ flows out of a relationship with Him. It's about experiencing God's grace, not earning His love through performance. A real relationship with Jesus Christ will produce a follower whose life looks progressively more like His life. Romans 12 provides a relational profile of an authentic disciple: someone who is surrendered to God, separate from the world's values, sober in self-assessment, serving in love and supernaturally responding to evil with good. Christians who live out this kind of lifestyle are what we call r12 Christians.

EFFECTIVE PARENTING IN A DEFECTIVE WORLD

Raising children is a tough challenge in today's world. Peers and pop culture exert a never-ending pressure on kids. Many come from split homes. But the good news is that God has been working with people from bad situations for a long time! In Effective Parenting you will learn how God's principles for raising children still work today. Packed with practical advice, this series will give struggling parents a vision for their children's future and life-changing help for today!

WHY I BELIEVE

An apologetic series to address your "honest doubts" and most pivotal questions about the claims of the Christian faith - What Happens When We Die? Can Miracles Be Explained? Is There Really A God? Answers to questions such as these are as varied as they are confusing and spring from a plethora of mystical belief systems. But the facts, we can know the truth. There are solid, logical answers to satisfy the heart and the mind of those who are seeking.

EXPERIENCING GOD'S DREAM FOR YOUR MARRIAGE

Would you like a fresh breeze to blow in your marriage? Do you long for a marriage where intimacy and communication are a reality instead of a dream? "Experiencing God's Dream for Your Marriage" is a topical series by Chip Ingram examining God's design for marriage, with practical instruction to help you make your marriage what God desires it to be.

FIVE LIES THAT RUIN RELATIONSHIPS

Have you ever looked back over a situation or relationship in your life and wondered how it became so messy or difficult? In Five Lies that Ruin Relationships, we'll define five of the most common lies that have the potential to ruin relationships with those we love. What we think about life determines how we live it, so there is power in knowing and applying God's truth when confronted with lies and discovering the freedom He longs for us to enjoy in our relationships.

LOVE, SEX & LASTING RELATIONSHIPS

Everyone wants to love and be loved. The pursuit of "true love" is everywhere you look! It's romanticized on TV and in the movies we watch. There are books about it, songs about it, internet dating, and even seminars on it... all of which are designed to "help" you find that special someone to love. So why is "true love" so elusive? Could it be that the picture of love we see in today's culture is nothing more than an illusion? If so, what does real love look like? In this series, you'll discover that there is a better way to find love, stay in love, and grow in intimacy for a lifetime. Chip Ingram delivers to us God's prescription for building relationships that last a lifetime.

BALANCING LIFE'S DEMANDS

Are you busy, tired, stressed out, and stretched to the limit? Does life seem a little out of control? Are you running long on "to do's" and short on time? If so, join us in this series, Balancing Life's Demands. You'll learn how to put "first things first" and find peace in the midst of pressure and adversity. No clichés or quick fixes, just practical biblical insights to help you order your personal world.

REBUILDING YOUR BROKEN WORLD

Lives today are filled with pain. Either through stress, pressure, unfortunate circumstances or bad decisions, many of us find ourselves living in a world that has fallen apart. This series from James 1 is designed to help you begin where you are and rebuild your broken world.

INVISIBLE WAR

Beneath our tangible landscape lurks an invisible spiritual realm where an unseen battle rages. It's real and it's dangerous. If you're prepared to remove the blinders and gaze into the unseen world, Chip is ready to take you there.

THE INTIMIDATION GAME

HOW THE LEFT IS SILENCING FREE SPEECH

KIMBERLEY STRASSEL

TWELVE

New York   Boston

Twelve
Hachette Book Group
1290 Avenue of the Americas
New York, NY 10104
twelvebooks.com
twitter.com/twelvebooks

First published in hardcover and ebook in June 2016
First trade paperback edition: June 2017

Twelve is an imprint of Grand Central Publishing.
The Twelve name and logo are trademarks of Hachette Book Group, Inc.

The publisher is not responsible for websites (or their content) that are not owned by the publisher.

The Hachette Speakers Bureau provides a wide range of authors for speaking events. To find out more, go to www.hachettespeakersbureau.com or call (866) 376-6591.

PCN: 2016937405

ISBNs: 978-1-4555-9189-3 (trade paperback), 978-1-4555-9190-9 (ebook)

Printed in the United States of America

LSC-C

10 9 8 7 6 5 4 3 2 1

To Oliver, Stella, and Frances—the loves of my life.
And to Alaska—for letting me dream again.

CONTENTS

INTRODUCTION

MOST PEOPLE wouldn't think of January 21, 2010, as an important date. It isn't Christmas. It isn't 9/11. It isn't a national holiday.

Yet that day marks a turning point in American politics.

January 21, 2010, is when the Supreme Court ruled on a case known as *Citizens United*. To listen to President Barack Obama, or Senator Harry Reid, or any number of self-proclaimed "good government" organizations, this decision mattered because it marked a new tidal wave of "dark" money and "shadowy" organizations into elections. It supposedly gave powerful special interests new control over democracy.

Citizens United didn't do any of that. But it did unleash a new era. It set off a new campaign of retribution and threats against conservatives. *Citizens United* launched the modern intimidation game.

Up to that day, Republicans and Democrats had played a different game, a familiar one. Both sides had spent a hundred years using speech laws, also known as campaign finance laws, to bar their respective opponents from taking part in elections. Democrats barred companies. Republicans barred unions. Democrats restricted right-leaning groups. Republicans restricted left-leaning groups. The laws kept piling up and up, until the Supreme Court could no longer justify the assault on the First

Amendment. *Citizens United* swept much of it away. Five justices restored the speech rights of millions of Americans.

The political right and libertarians mostly celebrated the decision as a triumph for democracy. The political left had the opposite reaction. Obama was on the ropes. He'd passed Obamacare, and Dodd-Frank, and a blowout stimulus spending bill— and America hadn't liked it. The party faced a wipeout in the 2010 elections. And now the high court had said Democrats could no longer legally shut up the companies and conservative nonprofits mobilizing against his party.

So the left moved to plan B. It moved to harass and scare and shame its opponents out of speaking.

Some in the liberal movement, including Obama and congressional Democrats, trained the federal government on opponents. They encouraged, explicitly and implicitly, the IRS to target and freeze conservative groups during election years. They called out conservative donors by name, making them the targets of a vast and threatening federal bureaucracy. They filed complaints with federal regulators and the Justice Department, calling on them to hassle or bar or prosecute their rivals. They came up with proposed executive orders and new IRS and SEC and FCC rules to order or frighten the other side out of the electoral process.

Powerful elected politicians used their positions to hold hearings into conservative political groups and to scare off donors to those operations. They sent letters to companies and think tanks and nonprofits, demanding to know who funded them, and whom they funded in turn. They launched investigations and leaked select details to the press. They flooded groups with document requests to drive up their costs and slow down their work. They made clear that those who donated "wrong" would end up on blacklists, or in front of Congress, or subject to boycotts.

Unions and liberal financial firms threatened to withdraw their money from companies that continued to speak. They pressured shareholders to force corporations to withdraw from the political scene. Activists camped outside CEOs' homes and staged rallies outside corporate headquarters.

Liberal prosecutors stepped up to threaten litigation against organizations that didn't hand over names of donors, so that those donors could be subject to the same treatment. Some prosecutors went much further: They sent armed police to march into houses in predawn raids, to let their opponents know that their exercise of free speech might land them in prison.

Liberal activists took to the streets—to urinate on houses, and block the entrances to stores, and stalk those who didn't agree with them on political issues. They left threatening telephone messages, and delivered ugly e-mails, and got people fired from their jobs for holding unpopular political views.

The intimidators embraced the tools that remained to them. They embraced disclosure laws, using the information they gleaned to create their lists of targets. They embraced arcane bits of campaign finance law, engineering new ways to persecute their opponents. They embraced the Internet and social media platforms, to launch protests, and badger free-market advocates, and even to create searchable, walkable maps that allowed them to harass people, one home at a time.

They also cleverly cloaked all this behind a claim of good government. *Citizens United*, they said, threatened to put powerful and nefarious forces in charge of democracy. And therefore all of their actions and tactics were justified in the name of the people. It was right to make Tea Party groups wait five years for permission to speak. It was right to send private investigators to dig into the divorce records of conservative donors. It was right to subject federal contractors to political litmus tests. It was right for prosecutors to issue gag orders. It was right to go to the Senate floor to vote to alter the First Amendment, and to put government in charge of speech. Getting rid of speech was for democracy's own good.

All these things happened. The stories are in this book. That they did happen, and are still happening, requires every American to rethink some conventional wisdom about the merits of speech and disclosure laws.

Nearly sixty years ago, the Supreme Court issued a groundbreaking decision, *NAACP v. Alabama*, that protected the rights of Americans to engage in politics with some degree of anonymity. This was the civil rights era, and blacks were being targeted, firebombed, and shot at for daring to speak out. The high court understood how corrosive this was to democracy, and declared that the Constitution provided some measure of refuge to citizens at risk of political retribution.

Yet the Court's brave stand slowly gave way to Nixon-era worries over electoral corruption. It rubber-stamped one campaign finance and disclosure law after another, eating away at its free-speech and anonymity legacy. Conservatives embraced the laws too, hoping to land on the right side of good-government history. In doing so, the conservative movement turbocharged its own muzzlers. Over time, the intimidators came to use the laws themselves—the ones supposedly designed to guard the electoral process—to intimidate.

Today, every American is at risk of retribution, because those who seek to control the debate do not make distinctions based on party affiliation. This book is largely about the new attempt by left-leaning organizations to shut down conservative speech. But the stories show that those who want absolute control over the debate are happy to silence anyone who proves a threat to their ideology.

They feel they must. Barack Obama ushered in a new era of liberal governance, yet one that has been rejected by significant numbers of Americans. The backlash brought the Democratic Party to new lows—to its smallest congressional and state majorities in nearly a century. Unable to win the debate in Washington, Obama has taken to imposing his will through executive orders. Unable to win the debate in the wider country, the liberal movement has decided to just shut it down.

This book chronicles the rise of those intimidation tactics—their genesis, their refinement, and the toll they've taken on free speech in America. The history is told through real stories, of real Americans, who faced silencing. The book as a result has almost accidentally become a record of the heroic attempts by those targeted to fight back, to make their voices heard, and to shore up the rights of their fellow citizens.

Those stories, though inspiring, ought to nonetheless be heard as a clarion call—particularly to the courts. In the 1950s, the high court recognized the stakes in the civil rights battle and felt compelled to secure the free-speech rights of black Americans. Today, Americans are again being targeted on the basis of their political views; they again risk losing their jobs and reputations for speaking out; they again face economic and community reprisal; they again face a government that is leading the charge to strip them of basic rights. Only this time, those who would shut them down are more powerful, and have more tools.

Indeed, today's environment is scarier. In the 1950s, the state and Jim Crow defenders had to work hard to conjure up a list of names of people to go after. They had to go to court. Today, all that information is available in a nanosecond, on any iPhone or computer, via any election disclosure site. Americans know this, and are increasingly scared to give to political causes, to join political groups. They have seen what happens. They know that if they take part, they will be called up, served up, beat up, and run out.

The intimidation game is working.